Chip Can Sit!

Kasia Reay

Illustrated by Clara Booth

Schofield&Sims

This is <u>Th</u>is is <u>Ch</u>ip the dog. He can beg.

He can run.

He can wag his t<u>ai</u>l.

He can beg and wag his tail.

No! No! No!

He can dig in the r<u>ai</u>n.

Yes, <u>C</u>hip can sit!

<u>Ch</u>ip the dog can sit wi<u>th</u> me.